This book belongs to

HOllY

Dad's Birthday and Other Stories

How this collection works

This *Biff, Chip and Kipper* collection is one of a series of four books at **Read with Oxford Stage 1**. It is divided into two distinct halves.

The first half focuses on phonics-based reading practice, with phonics activities in *Biff's Wonder Words* and *Floppy's Fun Phonics*. The second half contains three stories that use everyday language: *Floppy Did This!*, *Who Is It?* and *Dad's Birthday*. These stories help to broaden your child's wider reading experience. There are also fun activities to enjoy throughout the book.

How to use this book

Find a time to read with your child when they are not too tired and are happy to concentrate for about ten minutes. Reading at this stage should be a shared and enjoyable experience. It is best to choose just one story or phonics activity for each session.

There are tips for each part of the book to help you make the most of the activities and stories. The tips for reading on pages 6 and 28 show you how to introduce your child to the phonics activities.

The tips for reading on pages 50, 62 and 74 explain how you can best approach reading the stories that use a wider vocabulary. At the end of each story you will find four 'Talk about the story' questions. These will help your child to think about what they have read, and to relate the story to their own experiences. The questions are followed by a fun activity.

Enjoy sharing the stories!

Authors and illustrators

Biff's Wonder Words written by Kate Ruttle & Annemarie Young, illustrated by Alex Brychta
Floppy's Fun Phonics written by Kate Ruttle & Annemarie Young, illustrated by Nick Schon
Floppy Did This! written by Roderick Hunt, illustrated by Alex Brychta
Who Is It? written by Roderick Hunt, illustrated by Alex Brychta
Dad's Birthday written by Cynthia Rider, illustrated by Alex Brychta

OXFORD
UNIVERSITY PRESS

Great Clarendon Street, Oxford, OX2 6DP, United Kingdom

Oxford University Press is a department of the University
of Oxford. It furthers the University's objective of excellence
in research, scholarship, and education by publishing
worldwide. Oxford is a registered trade mark of Oxford
University Press in the UK and in certain other countries

Dad's Birthday text © Cynthia Rider 2005
Floppy Did This!, *Who is It?* text © Roderick Hunt 2006
Floppy's Fun Phonics, *Biff's Wonder Words* text © Kate Ruttle and Annemarie Young 2011

Dad's Birthday, *Floppy Did This!*, *Who Is It?*, *Biff's Wonder Words* illustrations © Alex Brychta 2005, 2006, 2011
Floppy's Fun Phonics illustrations © Nick Schon and Alex Brychta 2011

The characters in this work are the original creation of Roderick Hunt
and Alex Brychta who retain copyright in the characters

The moral rights of the authors have been asserted

Dad's Birthday first published in 2005
Floppy Did This! and *Who Is It?* first published in 2006
Floppy's Fun Phonics, *Biff's Wonder Words* first published in 2011
This Edition published in 2018

British Library Cataloguing in Publication Data
Data available

ISBN: 978-0-19-276416-4

10 9 8 7 6 5 4 3 2 1

Paper used in the production of this book is a natural, recyclable product
made from wood grown in sustainable forests. The manufacturing process
conforms to the environmental regulations of the country of origin.

Printed in China

Acknowledgements

Series Editors: Annemarie Young and Kate Ruttle

Contents

OXFORD
UNIVERSITY PRESS

Phonics

Children learn best when reading is relaxed and enjoyable.

- Tell your child they are going to help Biff to read words and play 'I spy'.

- Ask your child to read each of the words on the left-hand page. Then ask them to find them in the scene on the right-hand page.

- Once they have done this, ask them to do the activity on the right-hand page: find objects where the words start or end with a particular letter, or find words that rhyme.

- Don't forget that when you talk about letter sounds, say the letter sound clearly, for example, for the sound 'm', you say 'mmm' not 'em'. You can listen to the letter sounds at **oxfordowl.co.uk**.

- Give lots of praise as your child plays the game with you.

- Do the odd-one-out activity on each page and the spot the difference activity on page 26.

Have fun!

Find the odd one out on every left-hand page.

This story practises these letter sounds:

s a t p i n m d g o c
k ck e u r h b f ff ll ss

For more activities, free eBooks and practical advice to help your child progress with reading visit **oxfordowl.co.uk**

Biff's Wonder Words

cat
mud
dog

Read the words and find the pictures.

Hally

Help me read these words.
Can you find them in the picture?

Mum
Dad

dog, duck, door, drum, duckling, dandelion

Read these words and find them in the picture.

Holly

dog

cat

log, frog, bog

Read these words and find them in the picture.

mud

cap

web

water, wind, woodpecker

Read these words and find them in the picture.

bag

hat

pen

nut, mat, cat

Read these words and find them in the picture. Which words rhyme?

Holly **man**

bus

cab

van

can, pan

Read these words and
find them in the picture.

sun

cup

jam

log

Chip, cup, sheep

 Read these words and find them in the picture. Which words rhyme?

hen

bug

leg

den

den, pen

What else is in the picture that rhymes with **hen**?

Read these words and find them in the picture.

mop

pot

mug

lid

tap

pot, dot, fruit, bucket, biscuit

Read these words and find them in the picture.

Biff

rug

bed

mess

sock

clock, mug, head

Spot the difference

Find the five differences in the two pictures of Biff.

Tips for reading *Floppy's Fun Phonics*

Children learn best when reading is relaxed and enjoyable.

- Tell your child they are going to play a more difficult game of 'I spy'.

- On each page, read the instruction aloud, then ask your child to read the phrases on the left-hand pages and try to match them to the pictures on the right.

- Encourage your child to sound out the letters and say the words (e.g. *l-i-d, lid*).

- Your child will have to read carefully because some of the pages are tricky! Give them lots of praise.

- Do the odd-one-out activity on every left-hand page and the spot the difference activity on page 48.

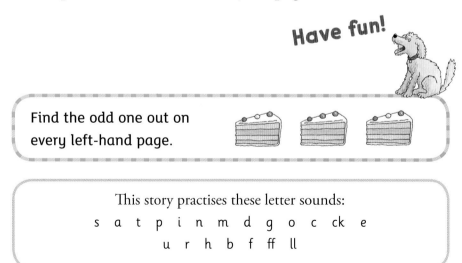

Have fun!

Find the odd one out on every left-hand page.

This story practises these letter sounds:

s   a   t   p   i   n   m   d   g   o   c   ck   e
u   r   h   b   f   ff   ll

For more activities, free eBooks and practical advice to help your child progress with reading visit **oxfordowl.co.uk**

Floppy's Fun Phonics

Match the puzzle pieces.

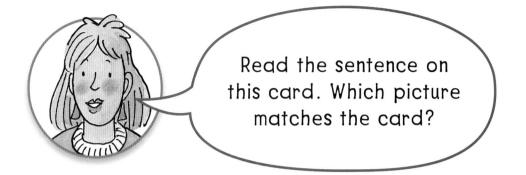

Read the sentence on this card. Which picture matches the card?

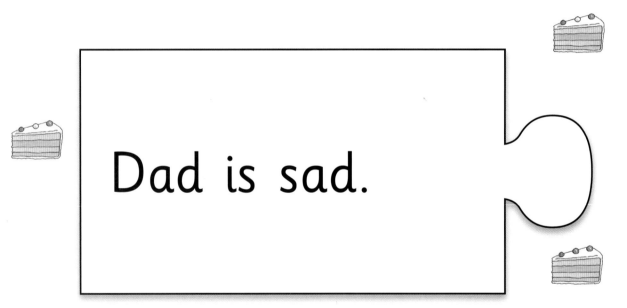

Dad is sad.

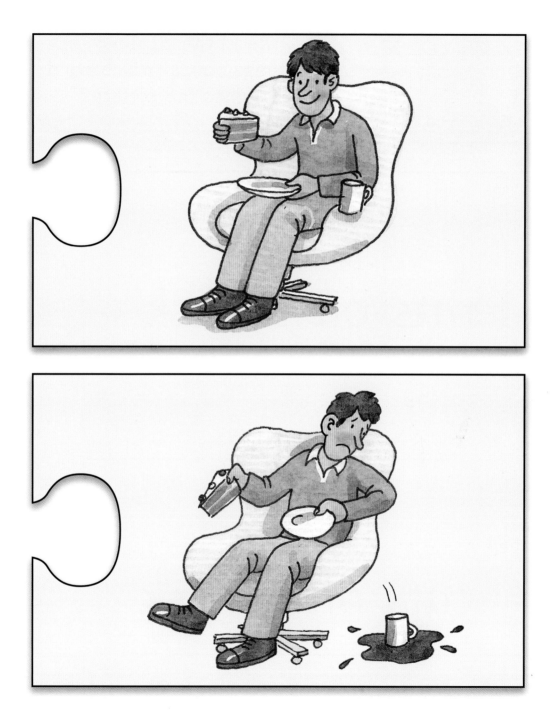

Read the captions on these cards. Which card matches the picture?

rats on a sack

cats on a sock

a hen and a bug

a hat on a dog

Read the sentences on these cards. Which card matches the picture?

Run in the sun.

Sit in the sun.

Read the sentences on these cards. Which card matches the picture?

A dog can sit.

A dog can run.

Read the sentences on these cards. Can you match each card to its picture?

A dog is a pet.

The dog is wet.

Read the sentences on these cards. Can you match each card to its picture?

Run and hop.

Run to the top.

Read the sentences on these cards. Can you match each card to its picture?

Biff is on a mug.

It is a big red bug.

Read the sentences on these cards. Can you match each card to its picture?

Biff is in a sack.

A doll is in a backpack.

Spot the difference

Find the five differences in the two pictures of Floppy.

Stories for Wider Reading

Tips for reading the stories together

These three stories use simple everyday language. Encourage your child to read as much as they can with you. You can help your child to read any more challenging words, like 'cake' and 'bike', in the context of the story. Children enjoy re-reading stories and this helps to build their confidence and their vocabulary.

Tips for reading *Floppy Did This!*

- Talk about the title and look through the pictures so that your child can see what the story is about.

- Read the story to your child, placing your finger under each word as you read.

- Read the story again and encourage your child to join in.

- Give lots of praise as your child reads with you.

- Talk about the story.

- Do the fun activity on page 60.

Have fun!

After you have read *Floppy did this!*, find the paintbrush in every picture.

This book includes these useful common words:

it   is   no

For more activities, free eBooks and practical advice to help your child progress with reading visit **oxfordowl.co.uk**

Floppy Did This!

Chip did this.

It is Biff.

Biff did this.

It is Kipper.

Kipper did this.

It is Mum.

Oh no!

Floppy did this!

Talk about the story

Who drew a picture of Kipper?

Why are they all clapping Floppy?

Which picture do you like best?

Who have you drawn pictures of?

Spot the difference

Find the five differences in the two pictures of Kipper.

Tips for reading *Who is it?*

- Talk about the title and look through the pictures so that your child can see what the story is about.

- Read the story to your child, placing your finger under each word as you read.

- Read the story again and encourage your child to join in.

- Give lots of praise as your child reads with you.

- Talk about the story.

- Do the fun activity on page 72.

For more activities, free eBooks and practical advice to help your child progress with reading visit **oxfordowl.co.uk**

Have fun!

Who is it?

Who is it?

It is Kipper.

Who is it?

It is Biff.

Who is it?

It is Chip.

Is it Kipper?

No. It is Floppy!

Talk about the story

What was Kipper dressed up as on page 64?

What was Biff doing on page 65?

What was the trick on page 69?

What do you like dressing up as?

Twins

Find the twin clowns.

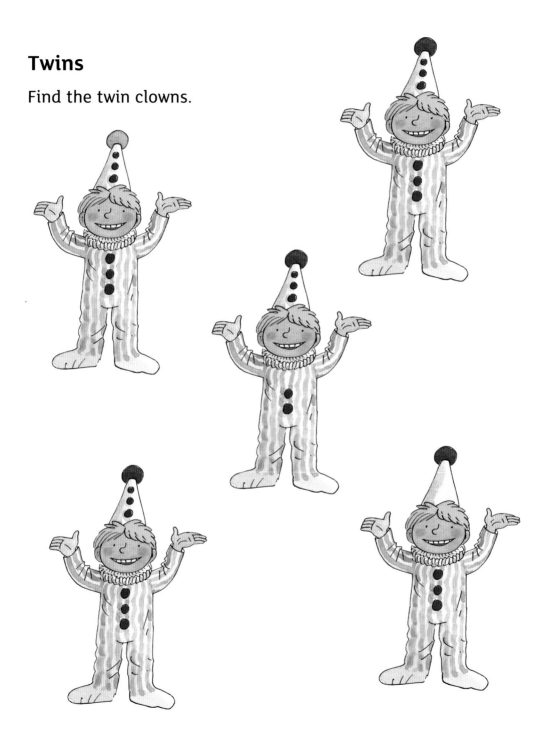

Tips for reading *Dad's Birthday*

- Talk about the title and look through the pictures so that your child can see what the story is about.
- Read the story to your child, placing your finger under each word as you read.
- Read the story again and encourage your child to join in.
- Give lots of praise as your child reads with you.
- Talk about the story.
- Do the fun activity on page 94.

Have fun!

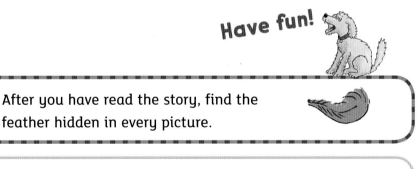

After you have read the story, find the feather hidden in every picture.

This story includes these useful common words:
go   had   on   Dad   said

For more activities, free eBooks and practical advice to help your child progress with reading visit **oxfordowl.co.uk**

Dad's Birthday

Dad had a birthday surprise.

It was Dad's birthday.

Dad had a cake.

He had a bike.

Dad got on the bike.

"Go on, Dad," said Biff.

"Go on, Dad," said Chip.

"Go on, Dad," said Kipper.

Dad fell off!

Oh no!

Talk about the story

How did Dad make the children laugh when he was on the bike?

Why did Dad fall off the bike? Why isn't it a good idea to stand on a bike like that?

How do you think everyone felt when Floppy ran away with the cake?

Do you like going to parties? What is the best party you have been to?

Matching

Match the parcels to the presents.

Remembering the stories together

Encourage your child to remember and retell the three stories in this book. You could ask questions like these:

- Who are the characters in the story?
- What happens at the beginning of the story?
- What happens next?
- How does the story end?
- What was your favourite part of the story? Why?

Story prompts

When talking to your child about the stories, you could use these more detailed reminders to help them remember the exact sequence of events. Turn the statements below into questions, so that your child can give you the answers. For example, *Who does Chip paint a picture of? Who paints a picture of Kipper?* And so on …

Floppy Did This!

- Chip paints a picture of Biff.
- Biff paints a picture of Kipper.
- Kipper paints a picture of Mum.
- Floppy makes his own painting!

Who Is It?

- Kipper is disguised as a clown doing tricks.

- Biff is disguised as a clown doing tricks.

- Chip is disguised as a clown doing tricks.

- Who is in the last disguise?

- It's Floppy!

Dad's Birthday

- The family are having a party for Dad in the garden.

- He blows out the candles on his cake.

- Dad opens his present. It's an exercise bike.

- He starts showing off and doing tricks on the bike.

- Oh no! He falls off and knocks everything over.

- Floppy catches the cake and makes a run for it!

You could now encourage your child to create a 'story map' of each story, drawing and colouring all the key parts of them. This will help them to identify the main elements of the stories and learn to create their own stories.